This book belongs to

_____

_____

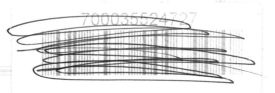

*With love to Zoe Kennedy, Gbenga Chesterman, William Evans
and Alice Harvey, who all got together for a change at Suzannah and
Lawrence's wedding – and helped to make their wish come true*

I.W.

For Jemma and Daniel, with love

First published in Great Britain in 2001 by Gullane Children's Books
This paperback edition published by

Gullane Children's Books

185, Fleet Street, London EC4A 2HS, United Kingdom
www.gulanebooks.com

3   5   7   9   10   8   6   4   2

Text © Ian Whybrow 2001. Illustrations © Tiphanie Beeke 2001

The right of Ian Whybrow and Tiphanie Beeke to be identified as the author and illustrator
of this work has been asserted by them in accordance with the Copyright, Designs, and Patents Act, 1988.

A CIP record for this title is available from the British Library.

ISBN 978-1-86233-738-1

Printed and bound in Indonesia

The Snow Friends

IAN WHYBROW

illustrated by
TIPHANIE BEEKE

GULLANE
CHILDREN'S BOOKS

Not many small pigs like reading. But Little Pig did.
He lived quietly on the edge of the wood,
under a big oak tree.

He had plenty
of acorns and twigs
and books, and for
a long time that was
enough for him.

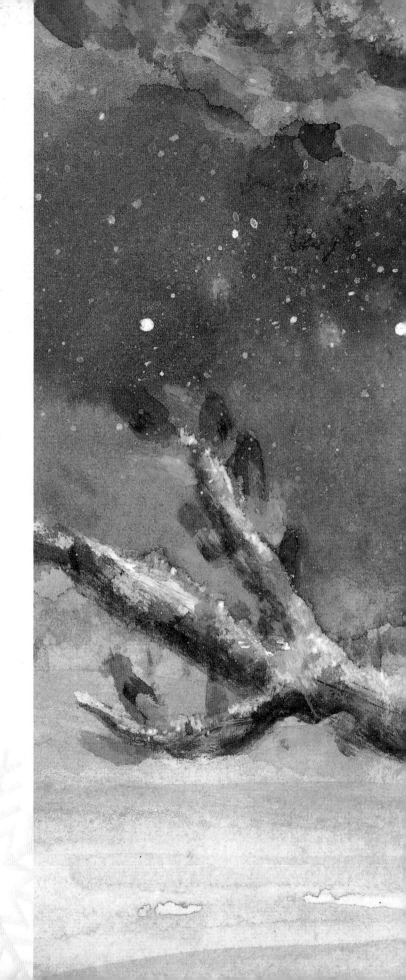

Then, one day,
he found three
new words in a book.

Wish was one.
That was easy.

The next was harder.
It was **change**.

The last was hardest.
It was **friend**.

Little Pig closed his eyes
and tried the words out.

"I *wish*
for a *change*
and a *friend*,"

he said to himself.

The **wish** worked. It started to snow.
And that was a nice **change**.

So Little Pig took
some acorns and some
twigs and some snow.
And he made a *friend*.

"Let's go," said
the snow friend.

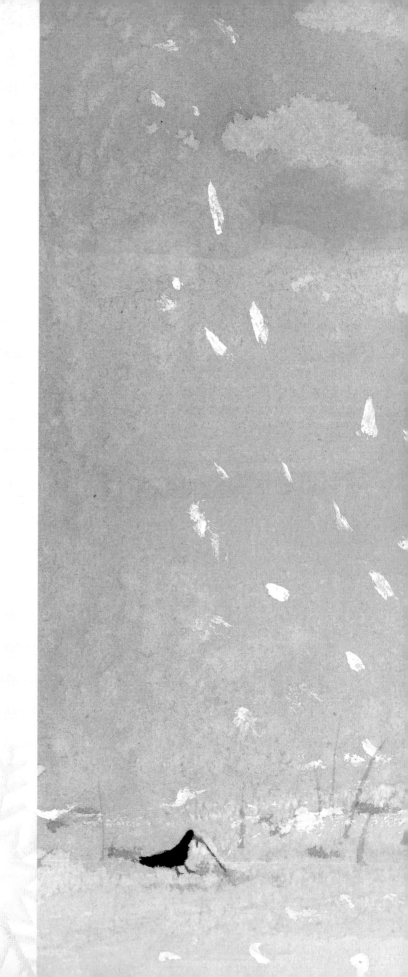

And off they went,
until they came to an igloo.

It was the home of a lonely bird.
He was reading a book.

The bird said to Little Pig
and his snow friend,
"Tell me, do you know these words?"

And he showed them **pig** and **together**.

"I am a **pig**," said Little Pig. "And my snow friend and I are **together**. What are you?"

And the lonely bird told him he was a **penguin**.

"Which word do you like best?" Little Pig asked.
"**Book**, *wish*, *change*, *friend*,
pig, *penguin*, or *together*?"

"I like them all," said Penguin.
"But best of all, I like **together**.
That one lasts the longest."

"We like that one best too,"
said Little Pig and his
snow friend, **together**.

IF YOU **WISH**
FOR A **CHANGE**,
GET **TOGETHER** HERE!
READ A BOOK OR
MAKE A NEW **FRIEND**!

Other books illustrated by
Tiphanie Beeke

Ferdie and the Falling Leaves
written by **Julia Rawlinson**

**Ferdie's
Springtime Blossom**
written by
Julia Rawlinson

From Me to You
written by **Anthony France**